BOBBY
Fr
ZOLTAN

MIKE
PUREWAL

AUSTIN MACAULEY PUBLISHERS™

LONDON • CAMBRIDGE • NEW YORK • SHARJAH

ISBN 9781398458840 (Paperback)
ISBN 9781398458857 (ePub e-book)

www.austinmacauley.com

First Published 2023
Austin Macauley Publishers Ltd®
1 Canada Square
Canary Wharf
London
E14 5AA

To Nina, thank you for encouraging me to follow my dreams and always having my back! Love you always.

"Are you Boban from Zoltan?
The magical wizard man!
I'm Dan your largest fan."

"Yes, I profess.
I am Boban from Zoltan.
I'll show my powers to you,
answering your questions too!"

"How does the world work, I need to see?
What is happening in my body?
Please tell me what is false and true."

"Great questions Dan, I'll give you every clue.

We will start with rain.
Oh the knowledge you'll gain!

I don't drop dogs big and small,
I don't drop ten thousand balls.
I don't drop candy or cake,
I don't drop cookies you bake.
I don't drop bikes or cars,
I don't drop gooey goop from mars.
I don't drop TVs and games,
I don't drop Meera or James!
I make sure it's water when it rains."

"Wow Boban from Zoltan,
that is true and not fake!
What happens when we awake?"

"You don't wake up in skyscrapers so tall,
you don't wake up in a very busy mall.
You don't wake up with toes on your face,
you don't wake up at the end of a race.
You don't wake up inside-out and upside-down,
you don't wake up next to one hundred clowns!
You don't wake up with three heads,
you don't wake up with three times the dreads!
I make sure you wake up in your bed."

"I see Boban from Zoltan.
I'm glad I wake up with my pet!
How does the sun rise and set?"

"That is a great question, Claire.
Here are more secrets I will share.

I make sure the sun causes the day to start.
I don't make the sun burp or fart!

I make sure the sun is nice and hot,
I don't make the sun full of snot.
I make sure the sun shines bright,
I don't make the sun and moon fight.
I make sure the sun warms us every spring,
I don't award the sun a championship ring!

Now in the exact same way,
order in nature exists every day.

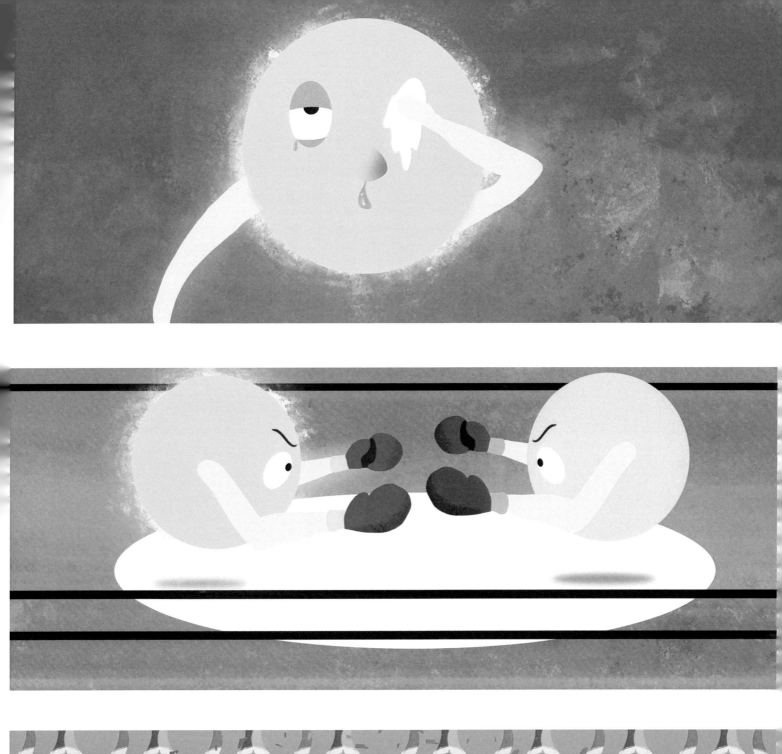

When you plant an apple seed,
a money tree doesn't grow that you need.
When a flower blossoms just right,
a large building doesn't appear at first sight.
When a blue jay hatches its eggs,
a caterpillar doesn't emerge with 250 legs.
When a baby turtle starts to grow,
it can't do backflips for good show!"

"Thanks Boban for showing me how the world runs!
I didn't realize your power with nature and the sun.
How do my body and senses work for good fun?"

"Sure thing Dan just sit tight,
You'll understand things right.

I gave you power for your eyes to see.
For this, I never charged you a fee!
When you see a roller coaster so big,
your eyes don't grow the size of a rig.
When you can't see in the dark,
your eyes don't disappear leaving no marks.
When you see the sun shining bright,
your eyes don't double bringing in more light.
When you see purple, pink and blue,
your eyes don't change with each colour
and hue.

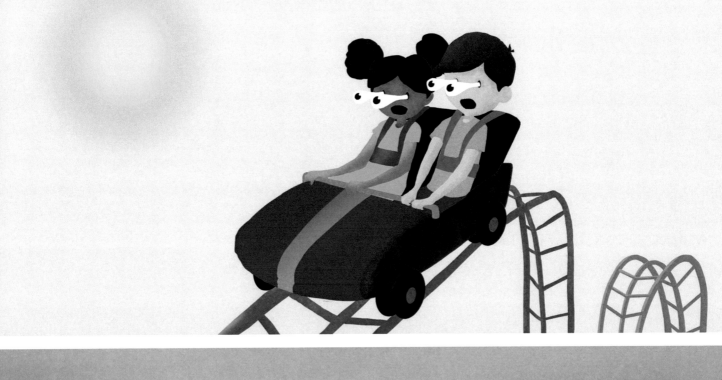

And now for example number two.
You smell the difference between flowers and poo!

I gave power for your nose to smell,
your nose can't scream and yell.
When you smell something so stinky and bad,
your nose doesn't frown and become very sad.

When you smell something of such delight,
your nose doesn't glow and turn very bright.
When you smell something far and away,
your nose doesn't fly there to play!"

"Boban from Zoltan you are wise and funny.
For my powers, you've not charged me money!
It must be true for touch, hearing and taste,
I'll never let my gratitude go to waste."

"Absolutely Claire, the senses make your brain think.
Big or small ideas don't make it grow or shrink.
You don't take brains out, washing them in the sink!
Or plug your brain into computers to charge.
The servers needed would be so very large!

Your heart pumps blood to make it all flow.
Seeing your pump, that would be a show.
Or needing gas to make the pump go!

Think about everything,
from the sun shining,
to nature changing,
while our body keeps growing!
I hope you appreciate this knowing."

"Thank you, Boban from Zoltan,
for the gifts given to each human.
If we know how lucky we have it,
we wouldn't feel sad, breaking that habit."

"Yes Dan, you are so right!
Think like this to stay light.
But if one day you feel down ready to fall,
remember me, I am the heart of it all."

"I love the world and my powers, I'm so thankful.
I'll never forget you and always be grateful!"

Mike Purewal worked in corporate for twenty years culminating as a Vice President of Sales. Along the way, he took the road less travelled by unplugging and living in the majestic Red Woods in Northern California for a year, studying happiness, mindfulness and meditation. This experience radically changed Mike's outlook on life and he is now following his passion of writing children's books that inspire humour, creativity and imagination. His ultimate goal is to bring more laughter and joy to the world for both children and adults alike. Mike currently lives in the greater Toronto area with his wife and daughter.

MIKEPUREWAL.COM

Instagram: @mike.purewal